Let's Visit The Lighth‹

MW00879619

Printed: June 2021 in Boca Raton, Florida

Author / Publisher

Ralph Krugler   *Ralph Krugler*

Illustrations By   Book Designer

Designersalam

9 781737 471226

A LONG TIME AGO,
NO ONE WAS AROUND.

THEN SUDDENLY ONE DAY,
THERE CAME SUCH A GREAT SOUND!

SO MUCH ACTIVITY,
PEOPLE MOVING ABOUT.
"WHAT ARE THEY BUILDING, "
SOMEONE DID SHOUT?

AT FIRST WE DIDN'T KNOW,
BUT SOON WE COULD SEE,
A STEAM ENGINE LIFTED PIECES,
SO EFFORTLESSLY.

THEY WORKED HARD EACH DAY,
AND SLEPT WELL EACH NIGHT.
THEN THEY WERE GONE,
AND OUT OF OUR SIGHT.

BRAND NEW LIGHTHOUSE,
STANDS PROUD ON THE SHORE.
WE COULDN'T HELP BUT WONDER,
WHAT WAS IT FOR?

THE SUN WENT DOWN,
AND DARKNESS DESCENDED,
THE ANSWER WAS THERE,
JUST AS INTENDED.

A BRILLIANT BRIGHT FLASH,
FROM THE TOP WE DID SEE.
THE LIGHT SPUN AROUND,
AND FAR OUT TO SEA.

HELPING SHIPS PASS,
ALL SAFE IN THE NIGHT.
THE SAILORS CHEERED,
WHEN THEY SAW THAT GRAND LIGHT.

LET'S GO TO THE LIGHTHOUSE,"
MY PARENTS DID SAY.
"TAKE WITH A PICNIC.
WE'LL MAKE IT A DAY."

WHEN WE ARRIVED,
WE LOOKED OUT TO THE SEA.
A SHIP WAS ARRIVING,
GLIDING EFFORTLESSLY.

A LIGHTHOUSE SHIP,
COMES TO DROP OFF SUPPLIES.
COMES EVERY SO OFTEN,
NOT A SURPRISE.

PEOPLE HAD COME,
FROM MILES AROUND,
TO GAZE IN WIDE WONDER,
AT WHAT WE HAD FOUND.

PEOPLE WERE SWIMMING,
OTHERS WERE FISHING.
AND EVERYONE FELT WELCOME,
TO SEE WHAT HAD BEEN MISSING.

WE MET THE LIGHTHOUSE KEEPER,
AND BOY WAS HE NICE.
HE SAID TO ASK QUESTIONS,
"PLEASE DON'T THINK TWICE ."

AFTER SOME THOUGHT
SOMEONE DID SAY,
"WHAT IS IT YOU DO HERE,
EVERY DAY?"

"THE STATION MUST BE SPOTLESS,
SO WE DUST AND WE MOP.
SOME THINGS NEED TO BE POLISHED,
BUT NOT A WHOLE LOT.

WE WORK IN THE DAY.
WE WORK THROUGH THE NIGHT.
WE TEND TO THE LIGHT,
MAKE SURE THAT IT'S BRIGHT."

THEN SOMEONE ELSE,
SHE WANTED TO KNOW,
"DO OTHERS TO HELP YOU,
OR ARE YOU SOLO?"

"TWO KEEPERS ASSIST ME,
THAT MAKES OUR COUNT THREE.
EACH HAS A FAMILY,
THAT LIVES HERE WITH ME."

"WHERE ARE YOUR CHILDREN,"
I WANTED TO KNOW?
"OFF IN THE BACK.
THEY SIT IN STRAIGHT ROWS."

KEEPER TURNED HIS STOREHOUSE,
INTO A SCHOOL ROOM ONE DAY.
SO THE CHILDREN DIDN'T HAVE TO GO,
OH SO FAR AWAY.

THEY LEARN AND THEY STUDY.
THEY PASS ALL THEIR TESTS.
EVERYONE SMILES,
THEY ALL DO THEIR BEST.

"CLASS ISN'T LONG,
BUT THEY LEARN OH SO MUCH.
WHEN THE LESSONS ARE DONE,
THEY'LL JOIN ALL OF US."

"THE LIGHTHOUSE HAS TWO COLORS,"
SAID A BOY IN THE BACK.
"IS THERE A REASON,
IT'S PAINTED LIKE THAT?" "

"WHEN YOU'RE OUT ON THE WATER,
AND LOOK TO THE SHORE,
THE COLORS STAND OUT.
THAT'S WHAT THEY'RE FOR."

A POPULAR QUESTION,
THAN AS IS NOW,
IS WHY IS THE LIGHTHOUSE,
SO HIGH OFF THE GROUND?

"SOME MAY BE TALL,
OTHERS QUITE SMALL,
EACH SERVES A PURPOSE,
TO HELP ONE AND ALL."

"WELL THAT'S GOOD FOR DAY,
BUT WHAT ABOUT AT NIGHT?
YOU CAN'T SEE COLORS,
OR EVEN THE HEIGHT."

"EACH LIGHTHOUSE IS DIFFERENT,
IN IT'S OWN SPECIAL WAY."
THIS IS WHAT,
THE KEEPER DID SAY.

"SOME LIGHTS HAVE COLORS,
THAT SHINE IN THE NIGHT.
EACH HAS A MEANING,
EACH MUST BE RIGHT.

MANY LIGHTS TURN,
THE SPEED IS THEIR OWN.
OTHERS ARE FIXED;
JUST LIKE IN YOUR HOME."

"A LIGHT IN MY HOUSE,
IS NEVER SO BRIGHT!
WHY DOES YOURS,
BEAM OUT IN THE NIGHT?"

THE KEEPER JUST POINTED,
AND SOMEONE DID GASP!
"IS THAT A BIG DIAMOND,
BEHIND ALL THAT GLASS?"

" THE KEEPER THEN SAID,
"THE LIGHT COMES FROM WITHIN.
THE CRYSTALS THEN GRAB IT,
WHICH MAKES US ALL GRIN.

THEN OUT THE BEAM GOES,
AND OH WHAT A SIGHT.
BE SURE TO LOOK.
IT'S ON EVERY NIGHT."

THEN WE CLIMBED UP,
ALL OF THOSE STAIRS.
WHEN WE ARRIVED,
NO ONE DID CARE.

NEXT TO THE LENS,
WE ALL FELT SO SMALL.
EVERYONE MARVELED,
MY IT'S SO TALL!

IT'S EASY TO SEE,
AS YOU GAZE AT THE SIGHT,
JUST WHAT MAKES THE LIGHT,
EVER SO BRIGHT.

"BUT HOW DOES IT TURN?
NO ONE CAN TELL."
"I'LL SHOW YOU CHILDREN.
YOU'LL THINK THAT IT'S SWELL."

"DOWN THROUGH THE TOWER,
A WEIGHT DOES DESCEND,
ATTACHED TO THE LENS,
AT THE OPPOSITE END.

THE WEIGHT GOES DOWN SLOWLY,
THROUGH THE CENTER IN FACT,
TILL ALMOST THE BOTTOM.
THEN WE CRANK IT UP FAST."

A QUESTION CAME,
FROM A CHILD IN THE BACK.
"ONCE IT'S ALL GOING,
WHERE DO YOU NAP?"

THE KEEPER DID CHUCKLE
AND WENT ON TO SAY,
"WE MUST STAY AWAKE,
FOR THAT IS OUR WAY.

WE MUST BE ALERT,
WATCH OUT FOR ANY TROUBLE.
FOR WHEN THAT HAPPENS,
WE'LL LEAVE ON THE DOUBLE."

"EVEN DURING STORMS,
LIKE HURRICANES AND SUCH?
OR DO YOU STAY HOME,
JUST LIKE ALL OF US?"

"WHEN THE WEATHER IS BAD,
WE'RE NEEDED THE MOST.
WE'LL ALWAYS BE HERE,
FOR THIS IS OUR POST.

IF SOMEONE NEEDS HELP,
WE'LL DO ALL THAT WE CAN.
KEEPING THE LIGHT SHINING,
IS NUMBER ONE PLAN."

WE THANKED HIM PROFUSELY,
FOR THE TIME THAT HE SPENT.
ALL THAT THEY DO,
WE'LL NEVER FORGET.

WE ALL WENT OUT,
LOOKED OVER THE SIDE.
NONE OF US,
HAD EVER BEEN OH SO HIGH.

JUST LIKE A BIRD,
WITH SUCH GREAT VISION.
THE KEEPER WAS OFF,
ON A NEW MISSION.

SWIFTLY HE WENT,
RAN OUT ON HIS BOAT;
TO HELP SOMEONE IN TROUBLE,
FAR OFF OF THE COAST.

WHEN HE RETURNED,
A SMILE WE DID SEE.
TOWING BEHIND HIM,
WHAT COULD THAT BE?

STRAPPED BEHIND HIM,
IT WASN'T A BOAT.
IT WASN'T A SHIP,
BUT BOY COULD IT FLOAT.

A SEAPLANE HAD COME DOWN,
RIGHT OUT OF THE SKY,
THREE PEOPLE ABOARD,
NO ONE NEEDED TO CRY.

EVERYONE WAS SAFE,
AND NOW ON THE LAND.
THE KEEPER DID SAVE THEM,
WE GAVE HIM A HAND.

WHEN THAT WAS OVER,
WE ALL HAD MORE FUN.
LAUGHING AND PLAYING,
SOME LAY IN THE SUN.

WE SAW SOME TURTLES,
A GREAT NUMBER OF FISH.
THEN SOMEONE RECEIVED
THEIR GREATEST WISH.

A MANATEE FAMILY
SWAM SLOWLY PAST.
MOVING SO GRACEFULLY,
NOT ONE WAS FAST.

THE END OF THE DAY.
TIME TO DEPART.
NOT BEFORE HELPING,
CLEAN UP THE YARD.

THE KEEPERS ALL WANT,
THE STATION CLEAN AS CAN BE.
WHEN THE INSPECTOR COMES,
ALL HAS TO BE TIDY.

EVERYTHING IS CLEAN,
AND IN ITS OWN PLACE.
OUR KEEPERS THEY WERE,
NEVER A DISGRACE.

THEY WON MANY AWARDS,
FOR AN EFFICIENT STATION.
AND EVERY ONE PRAISED THEM,
ALL ACROSS THE NATION.

SO FROM ALL OF THE KEEPER'S,
AND ALL THEIR NEW FRIENDS.
WE THANK YOU FOR READING,
SAY TO YOUR FRIENDS.

*"LET'S GO TO THE LIGHTHOUSE,
WE'LL LAUGH AND WE'LL PLAY."*
WE'LL SEE YOU AGAIN,
HAVE A GREAT DAY!

Made in the USA
Monee, IL
24 May 2022

96957330R00024